# A Poison Tree

poems selected by

Pie Corbett and Valerie Bloom

# DAD

Dad is the dancing-man
The laughing-bear, the prickle-chin,
The tickle-fingers, jungle-roars
Bucking bronco, rocking-horse,
The helicopter roundabout
The beat-the-wind at swing-and-shout
Goal-post, scarey-ghost
Climbing-Jack, humpty-back.

But sometimes he's
A go-away-please!
A snorey-snarl, a sprawly-slump
A yawny mouth, a sleeping lump,

And I'm a kite without a string
Waiting for Dad to dance again.

*Berlie Doherty*

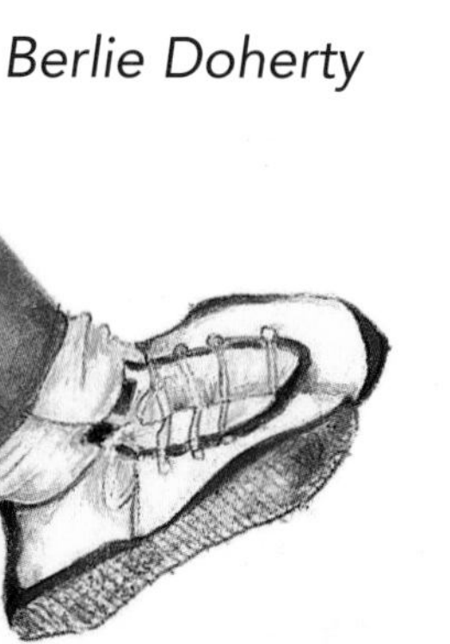

# What Dads Do

Make bookshelves.
Make burgers.
Make money.
Make funny faces that make you laugh.
Scratch your back when you can't reach where it itches.
Lift you up on their shoulders.
Snore when they're sleeping (but say they don't).
Pitch – but not so fast that you can't hit their pitches.

Play tickles with you when you feel like a silly person.
Snuggle up close with you when you feel like a sad one.
Dads explain electricity
And peninsulas
And help you count the stars.

I wish I still had one.

*Judith Viorst*

# The Secret Brother

Jack lived in the green-house
When I was six,
With glass and with tomato plants,
Not with slates and bricks.

I didn't have a brother,
Jack became mine.
Nobody could see him,
He never gave a sign.

Just beyond the rockery,
By the apple-tree,
Jack and his mother lived,
Only for me.

With a tin telephone
Held beneath the sheet,
I would talk to Jack each night.
We would never meet.

Once my sister caught me,
Said, "He isn't there.
Down among the flower-pots
Cramm the gardener

Is the only person."
I said nothing, but
Let her go on talking.
Yet I moved Jack out.

He and his old mother
Did a midnight flit.
No one knew his number:
I had altered it.

Only I could see
The sagging washing-line
And my brother making
Our own secret sign.

*Elizabeth Jennings*

# What Has Happened to Lulu?

What has happened to Lulu, mother?
  What has happened to Lu?
There's nothing in her bed but an old rag-doll
  And by its side a shoe.

Why is her window wide, mother,
  The curtain flapping free,
And only a circle on the dusty shelf
  Where her money-box used to be?

Why do you turn your head, mother,
  And why do the tear-drops fall?
And why do you crumple that note on the fire
  And say it is nothing at all?

I woke to voices late last night,
  I heard an engine roar.
Why do you tell me the things I heard
  Were a dream and nothing more?

I heard somebody cry, mother,
  In anger or in pain,
But now I ask you why, mother,
  You say it was a gust of rain.

Why do you wander about as though
  You don't know what to do?
What has happened to Lulu, mother?
  What has happened to Lu?

*Charles Causley*

# My Sparrow Gran

My sparrow gran
Is the singing one
Busy and tidy
And brown-bright-eyed
She chirrups and chats
She scurries and darts
She picks up the bits
That clutter her nest
And when evening comes
When all her work's done
I bring her my book
And sit on her lap
Snug in her arms
That are feather-down warm.

*Berlie Doherty*

# The Living Photograph

My small grandmother is tall there,
straight-back, white broderie anglaise shirt,
pleated skirt, flat shoes, grey bun,
a kind, old smile round her eyes.
Her big hand holds mine,
white hand in black hand.
Her sharp blue eyes look her own death in the eye.

It was true after all; that look.
My tall grandmother became small.
Her back round and hunched.
Her soup forgot to boil.
She went to the awful place grandmothers go.
Somewhere unknown, unthinkable.

But there she is still,
in the photo with me at three,
the crinkled smile is still living, breathing.

Jackie Kay

# Volcano

smoke
heat gas flame
rocks heat
flame
fire fi
eee E eee
gas
xxx X xxx X xxx X xxx
f i re pppppppppppppp p pppppppppppppp
he ||||||||||||||||||||| L ||||||||||||||||||||| gas
a ooooooooooo O ooooooooooo rocks
L sssssssssssssss S sssssssssssssss
t iiiiiiiiiiiiiiiiiiiiiiiii I iiiiiiiiiiiiiiiiiiiiiiiii m
k ooooooo O ooooooo L
s nnnn N nnnn g
E! press V
m RE! pressure VO r
la IRE! pressure VOL
va FIRE! pressure VOLC la
C FIRE! pressure VOLCA va
IC FIRE! pressure VOLCAN
NIC FIRE! pressure VOLCANI
ANIC FIRE! pressure VOLCANIC
CANIC FIRE! pressure VOLCANIC F
LCANIC FIRE! pressure VOLCANIC FI
OLCANIC FIRE! pressure VOLCANIC FIR
VOLCANIC FIRE! pressure VOLCANIC FIRE!

*Mary Green*

# Flight Path

I need no calendar:
one day in late Summer,
something in the light tilts;
the weather speaks deep
in my blood and feathers,
tells me it's time to go.

I need no map, no lodestar:
the route home is printed
here in my curved wings;
my flight is urgent, slanted
free as the trade winds
singing *Africa*, *Africa*.

*Tony Charles*

# The Charge of the Light Brigade

(an extract)

Half a league, half a league,
Half a league onward,
All in the valley of Death
Rode the six hundred.
"Forward, the Light Brigade!
Charge for the guns!" he said.
Into the valley of Death
Rode the six hundred.

"Forward, the Light Brigade!"
Was there a man dismayed?
Not though the soldier knew
Some one had blundered.
Theirs not to make reply,
Theirs not to reason why,
Theirs but to do and die.
Into the valley of Death
Rode the six hundred.

Cannon to right of them,
Cannon to left of them,
Cannon in front of them
Volleyed and thundered;
Stormed at with shot and shell,
Boldly they rode and well,
Into the jaws of Death,
Into the mouth of Hell
Rode the six hundred.

*Alfred, Lord Tennyson*

# THE HUNTSMAN

*The story is based on a folk tale heard by the author in Kenya in 1944.*

Kagwa hunted the lion,
  Through bush and forest went his spear.
One day he found the skull of a man
  And said to it, "How did you come here?"
The skull opened its mouth and said
  "Talking brought me here."

Kagwa hurried home;
  Went to the king's chair and spoke:
"In the forest I found a talking skull."
  The king was silent. Then he said slowly
"Never since I was born of my mother
  Have I seen or heard of a skull which spoke."

The king called out his guards:
  "Two of you now go with him
And find this talking skull:
  But if his tale is a lie
And the skull speaks no word,
  This Kagwa himself must die."

**They rode into the forest:**
**For days and nights they found nothing.**
**At last they saw the skull; Kagwa**
**Said to it "How did you come here?"**
**The skull said nothing. Kagwa implored,**
**But the skull said nothing.**

**The guards said "Kneel down."**
**They killed him with sword and spear.**
**Then the skull opened its mouth;**
**"Huntsman, how did you come here?"**
**And the dead man answered**
**"Talking brought me here."**

*Edward Lowbury*

# The Quarrel

I quarrelled with my brother
I don't know what about,
One thing led to another
And somehow we fell out.
The start of it was slight,
The end of it was strong,
He said he was right,
I knew he was wrong!

We hated one another.
The afternoon turned black.
Then suddenly my brother
Thumped me on the back,
And said, "Oh, *come* along!
We can't go on all night –
I was in the wrong."
So he was in the right.

*Eleanor Farjeon*

# A Poison Tree

*I was angry with my friend:*
*I told my wrath, my wrath did end.*
*I was angry with my foe:*
*I told it not, my wrath did grow.*

*And I watered it in fears,*
*Night and morning with my tears;*
*And I sunnèd it with smiles,*
*And with soft deceitful wiles.*

*And it grew both day and night,*
*Till it bore an apple bright;*
*And my foe beheld it shine,*
*And he knew that it was mine,*

*And into my garden stole*
*When the night had veiled the pole:*
*In the morning glad I see*
*My foe outstretched beneath the tree.*

William Blake

# The Inchcape Rock

*1. The Inchcape Bell*

No stir in the air, no stir in the sea,
The ship was still as she could be,
Her sails from heaven received no motion,
Her keel was steady in the ocean.

Without either sign or sound of their shock
The waves flowed over the Inchcape Rock;
So little they rose, so little they fell,
They did not move the Inchcape Bell.

The Abbot of Aberbrothok
Had placed that bell on the Inchcape Rock;
On a buoy in the storm it floated and swung,
And over the waves its warning rung.

When the Rock was hid by the surge's swell,
The mariners heard the warning bell;
And then they knew the perilous Rock
And blest the Abbot of Aberbrothok.

*2. Sir Ralph the Rover's Wicked Deed*

The sun in heaven was shining gay,
All things were joyful on that day;
The sea-birds screamed as they wheeled round,
And there was joyaunce in their sound.

The buoy of the Inchcape Bell was seen
A darker speck on the ocean green;
Sir Ralph the Rover walked his deck,
And he fixed his eye on the darker speck.

He felt the cheering power of spring;
It made him whistle, it made him sing;
His heart was mirthful to excess.
But the Rover's mirth was wickedness.

His eye was on the Inchcape float;
Quoth he, "My men, put out the boat,
And row me to the Inchcape Rock,
And I'll plague the Abbot of Aberbrothok."

The boat is lowered, the boatmen row,
And to the Inchcape Rock they go.
Sir Ralph bent over from the boat,
And he cut the Bell from the Inchcape float.

Down sunk the Bell with a gurgling sound,
The bubbles rose and burst around;
Quoth Sir Ralph, "The next who comes to the Rock
Won't bless the Abbot of Aberbrothok."

*3. Sir Ralph the Rover's Return*

Sir Ralph the Rover sailed away,
He scoured the seas for many a day;
And now grown rich with plundered store,
He steers his course for Scotland's shore.

So thick a haze o'erspreads the sky
They cannot see the sun on high;
The wind hath blown a gale all day,
At evening it hath died away.

On the deck the Rover takes his stand,
So dark it is they see no land.
Quoth Sir Ralph, "It will be lighter soon
For there is the dawn of the rising Moon."

"Canst hear," said one, "the breakers roar?
For methinks we should be near the shore."
"Now where we are I cannot tell.
But I wish I could hear the Inchcape Bell."

They hear no sound, the swell is strong:
Though the wind hath fallen, they drift along.
Till the vessel strikes with a shivering shock. –
"Oh, Christ! It is the Inchcape Rock!"

Sir Ralph the Rover tore his hair;
He cursed himself in his despair;
The waves rush in on every side,
The ship is sinking beneath the tide.

But even in his dying fear
One dreadful sound could the Rover hear,
A sound as if with the Inchcape Bell
The Devil below was ringing his knell.

*Robert Southey*

# My Kind of School

Deep in the forest
Where a cool breeze
Fans my face,
Where the warm sun
Shines in bright
Geometry problems
Through the leaves
While birds lecture and scold
And squirrels play at recess
Through the trees –
This is my kind of school.

Or give me
A great rock ledge
Overlooking a valley.
Below me, let me study
People as they rush about
As if today stands alone –
Their only time
For running past
Their neighbours.
And still I sit
In quietness,
Learning from them
That to run
Is to run,
Is to run ...

*Raymond Teeseteskie*
*(American Indian – Cherokee)*

# Eleven Years Old

I'm old enough
to work in the fields,
my grandmother says:
your limbs are young
and strong,
your mind won't rust,
we need the extra hands
to tend the crop
and feed the goats
and till this ungrateful land.

Maybe
I'll go to school
when the crop is in,
when we take the few yams
from the soil,
then I'll wear a new dress,
and leave when it's early day,
for it's only one mile to the school.

*Dionne Brand*
*(Trinidad)*

# Child-body Starving Story

Head misshapen and patchy with hair
  with shocked eyes in a hole with a stare

cheeks collapsed in skin among bones
  with cracked lips having not one moan

ears keeping a nonstop whining sound
  with neck hardly more than a broom-handle hold

hunched up shoulders v-shaped
  with twiggy arms claws-fingered

a belly all self pumped-up
  and knees the knotted marbles thinly skin wrapped

legs the drumsticks knee-knockers
  with feet not finding a body to carry together –

show me off, as this body-exhibit labelled,
'A NOT-ENOUGH-TO-SHARE LEFT-OUT'
and other times labelled,
'A GOVERNMENTS' NON-CARING LEFT-OUT'.

*James Berry*

*(African-Caribbean/British)*

# Haircut Rap

Ah sey, ah want it short,
Short back an' side,
Ah tell him, man, ah tell him
When ah teck him aside,
Ah sey, ah want a haircut
Ah can wear with pride,
So lef' it long on top
But short back an' side.

Ah sey try an' put a pattern
In the shorter part,
Yuh could put a skull an' crossbone,
Or an arrow through a heart.

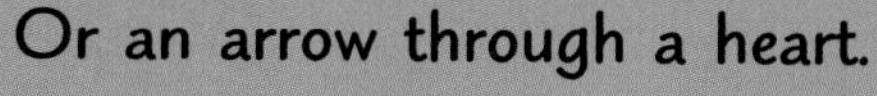

Meck sure ah have enough hair lef'
Fe cover me wart,
Lef a likkle pon the top,
But the res' – keep it short.

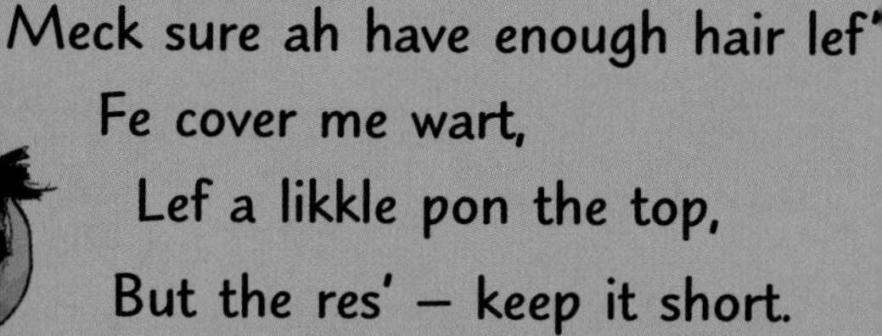

Well, bwoy, him start to cut
An' me settle down to wait.
Him was cuttin' from seven
Till half-past eight.
Ah was startin' to get worried
'Cause ah see it gettin' late,
But then him put the scissors down,
Sey, "There yuh are, mate."

Well, ah did see a skull an' a
Criss-cross bone or two,
But was me own skull an' bone
That was peepin' through.
Ah look jus' like a monkey
Ah did see once at the zoo,
Him say, "What's de matter, Tammy,
Don't yuh like the hair-do?"

Well, ah feel me heart stop beatin'
When me look pon me reflection,
Ah feel like somet'ing frizzle up
Right in me middle section.
Ah look aroun' fe somewhey
Ah could crawl an' hide,
The day I meck me brother cut
Me hair short back an' side.

*Valerie Bloom*

# If You Have Time

If you have time to chatter
Read books

If you have time to read
Walk into mountain, desert and ocean

If you have time to walk
Sing songs and dance

If you have time to dance
Sit quietly, you Happy Lucky Idiot.

*Nanao Sakaki*
*(Japan)*

# Index of Titles